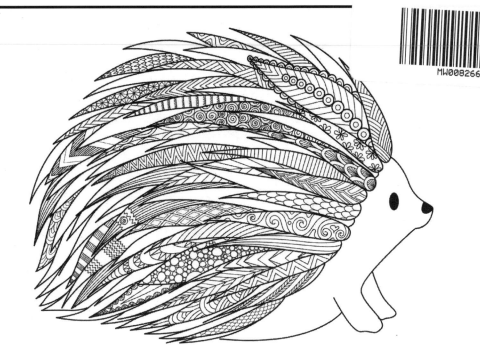

Hedgehog
Coloring Book

CREATIVE COLORING PRESS

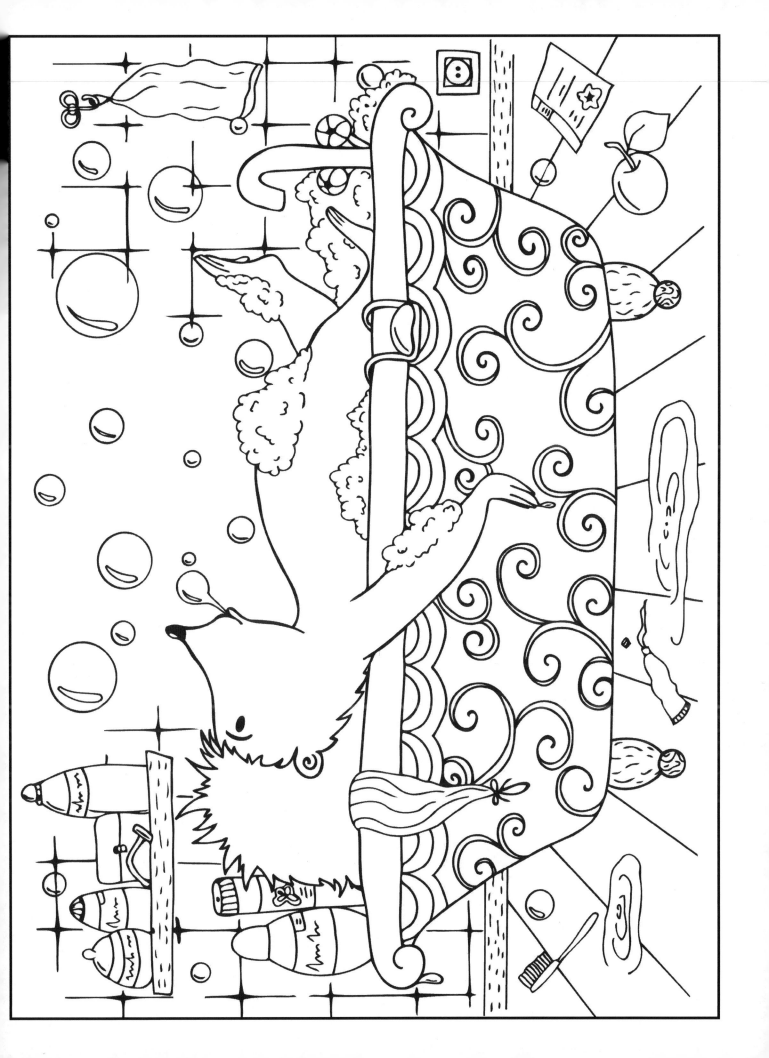

Thank you for purchasing this coloring book! I hope that you enjoy coloring it as much as we enjoyed creating it. Please consider leaving a review, we really appreciate hearing your opinion!

Sign-Up to Get a Free Coloring Book

Subscribe to our newsletter and get a free printable coloring book of some of our most popular illustrations. Plus you'll receive special offers, sneak peeks at new releases, and more.
Visit us at **www.creativecoloring.co** for details.

We want to hear from you!

We hope you've enjoyed this coloring book and that is brings you many hours of fun, stress relief, and creativity. We'd love to see and share your creations.

Send us your ideas, suggestions, and finished artwork:

www.creativecoloring.co
facebook.com/creativecoloringpress
Instagram: @creativecoloringpress
Twitter: @creativecoloringpress

Bonus

Turn the page for bonus pages from some of our most popular coloring books.

COLORFUL
HORSE
COLORING BOOK

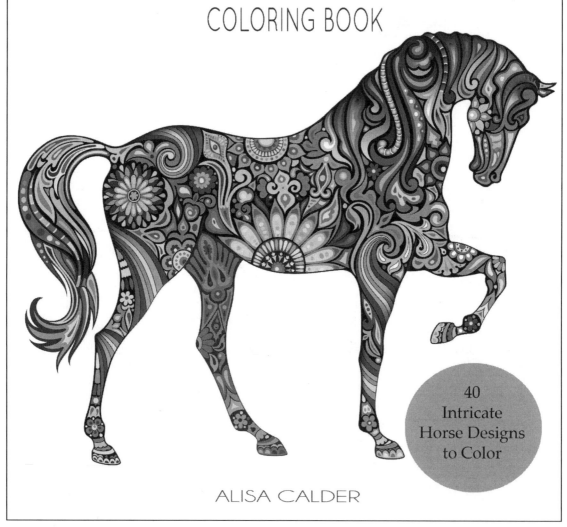

40
Intricate
Horse Designs
to Color

ALISA CALDER

Colorful Horse Coloring Book by Alisa Calder.
Available now at Amazon.com, Barnes and Noble, and other online retailers.

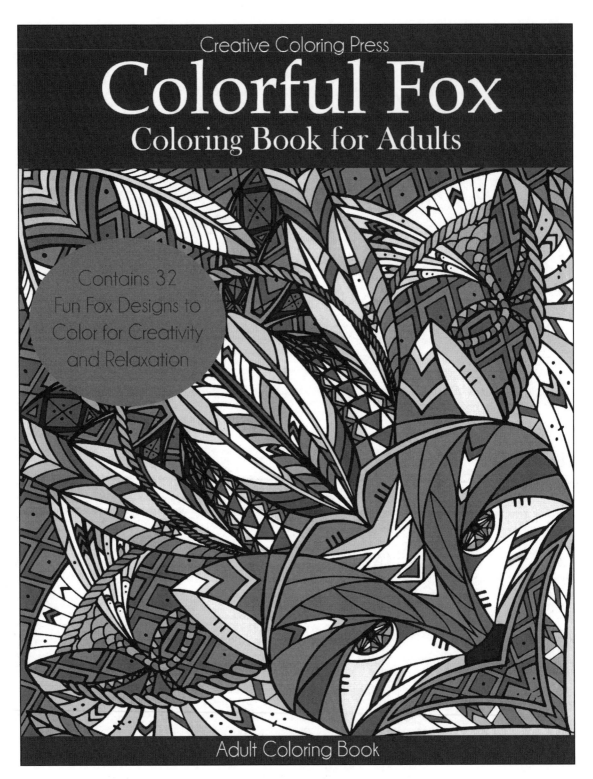

Colorful Fox by Creative Coloring Press.
Available now at Amazon.com, Barnes and Noble, and other online retailers.

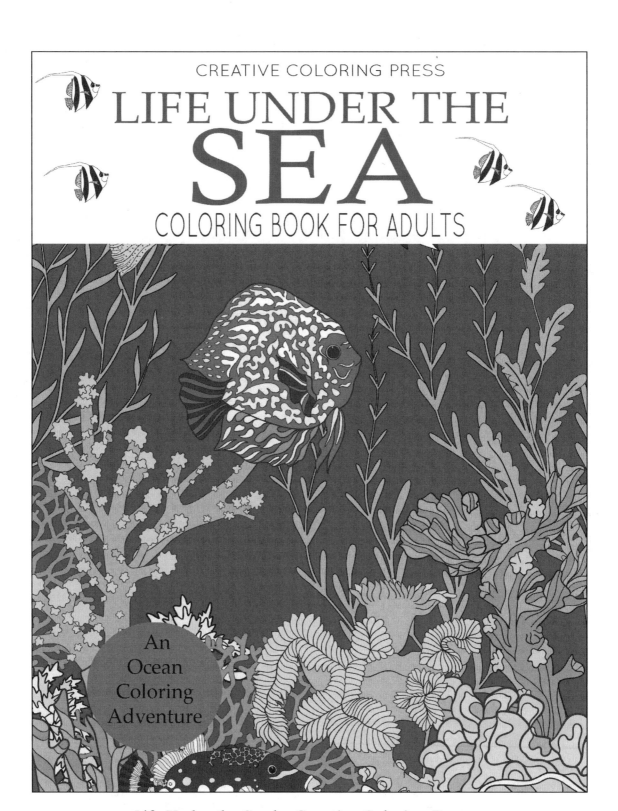

Life Under the Sea by Creative Coloring Press.
Available now at Amazon.com, Barnes and Noble, and other online retailers.

Made in the USA
Middletown, DE
20 December 2024

67832970R00046